Jolly Jumping Jelly Beans

Story by Jan McPherson

A hippo with a hat.
A hippo with a hat.
Jolly jumping jelly beans!
How about that!

A rabbit with a hat.
A rabbit with a hat.
Jolly jumping jelly beans!
How about that!

A whale with a hat.
A whale with a hat.
Jolly jumping jelly beans!
How about that!

A bat with a hat.
A bat with a hat.
Jolly jumping jelly beans!
How about that!

An emu with a hat.
An emu with a hat.
Jolly jumping jelly beans!
How about that!

A monkey with a hat.
A monkey with a hat.
Jolly jumping jelly beans!
How about that!

A cat with a hat. . .

and a hat with a cat!

Jolly hats and jelly beans!
How about that!